CONTENTS

ALEXANDER-GRACE EDUCATION

Understanding the MAP Tests

The NWEA MAP (Measures of Academic Progress) test is an adaptive assessment that is designed to measure student growth and progress in a variety of subject areas. The test is taken by millions of students across the United States and is widely used by educators to help inform instruction and measure student outcomes. The NWEA MAP test is administered online and provides immediate feedback on student performance, allowing teachers to adjust their teaching strategies and provide targeted support to individual students.

The NWEA MAP test is unique in that it is adaptive, which means that the difficulty of the questions adjusts based on the student's responses. This allows the test to be more personalized to each student's abilities and provides a more accurate measure of their knowledge and skills. The test covers a range of subject areas, including mathematics, reading, language usage, and science, and is administered multiple times throughout the school year. This allows teachers to track student progress and growth over time and make data-driven decisions to improve student outcomes.

Purpose and Benefits of MAP Testing

The primary purpose of the MAP Test is to provide valuable insights into a student's learning and academic progress. By offering a detailed analysis of a student's performance in reading, language usage, mathematics, and science, the test helps teachers tailor their instruction to meet individual needs. The MAP Test also serves as a benchmarking tool, allowing schools and districts to compare their students' performance with national norms and other local institutions.

This data-driven approach enables educators to make informed decisions about curriculum, instructional methods, and resource allocation, ultimately leading to improved student outcomes. Additionally, the MAP Test can help identify gifted students who may benefit from advanced or accelerated programs, as well as students who may require additional support or interventions.

Test Format and Content

The MAP Test is divided into four primary content areas: reading, language usage, mathematics, and science. Each section consists of multiple-choice questions that cover various topics and skills within the respective subject. The test is untimed, allowing students to work at their own pace and ensuring a lower level of test anxiety. The computer-adaptive nature of the MAP Test ensures that the difficulty of questions adjusts based on a student's performance, making it suitable for students of all ability levels. As a result, the MAP Test not only evaluates a student's mastery of grade-level content but also assesses their readiness for more advanced material.

Adaptive Testing and Scoring System

One of the unique aspects of the MAP Test is its adaptive testing system. As students answer questions, the test adjusts the difficulty of subsequent questions based on their performance. This adaptive nature allows the test to home in on a student's true ability level, providing more accurate and meaningful results. The MAP Test uses a RIT (Rasch Unit) scale to measure student achievement, which is an equal-interval scale that allows for easy comparison of scores across grade levels and subjects. This scoring system allows educators and parents to track a student's growth over time, making it an invaluable tool for understanding academic progress and setting individualized learning goals.

Preparing for Success on the MAP Test

Effective preparation for the MAP Test involves a combination of understanding the test format, mastering content knowledge, and developing test-taking strategies. This test prep book is designed to provide students with comprehensive guidance on each content area, offering targeted instruction and practice questions to build confidence and ensure success. Additionally, the book includes test-taking tips and strategies to help students approach the test with a calm and focused mindset. By working through this book and dedicating time to consistent practice, students will be well-equipped to excel on the MAP Test and achieve their academic goals.

Note that, since there is no cap to the level that a student can work to in preparation for this test, there is no 'completion' of content, as students can simply do questions from grades above in preparation. It should be noted that students are not expected to work far above grade level to succeed in this test, as consistent correct answers are more relevant.

What Is Contained Within this Book?

Within this book you will find 320 questions based off content which would be found within the MAP test your student will take. The content found in this book will be the equivalent of grade 8 level. Note that since this test is adaptive, some students may benefit by looking at several grade levels of content, not just their own.

At the end of the book will contain answers alongside explanations. It is recommended to look and check your answers thoroughly in regular intervals to make sure you improve as similar questions come up.

Topic 1 – Equations

1.1) Solve for x: $3x + 5 = 20$

□ $x = -5$

□ $x = 10$

□ $x = 5$

□ $x = 15$

1.2) Solve for y: $2(y - 3) + 4 = 10$

□ $y = 3$

□ $y = 5$

□ $y = 6$

□ $y = 4$

1.3) If $4x - 2 = 2x + 6$, what is the value of x?

□ $x = 1$

□ $x = 2$

□ $x = 4$

□ $x = 8$

1.4) Solve for x: $x/2 + 7 = 15$

□ $x = 8$

□ $x = 16$

□ $x = 6$

□ $x = 4$

1.5) Solve the equation: $5x - (2x + 3) = 10$

□ $x = 3$

□ $x = 4.3$

□ $x = 6.5$

□ $x = 2.6$

1.6) Solve for x: $3(x + 4) - 5x = 2$

□ $x = 5$

□ $x = -14$

□ $x = 14$

□ $x = -10$

1.7) What is the solution to the equation: $x/3 - 2 = 4$

□ $x = -18$

□ $x = 6$

□ $x = 18$

□ $x = -6$

1.8) Solve for x: $5(x - 2) = 3(x + 4)$

□ $x = 20$

□ $x = 0$

□ $x = -10$

□ $x = 11$

1.9) Solve the equation: $2(x + 5) = x - 3$

□ $x = 13$

□ $x = -8$

□ $x = -13$

□ $x = 8$

1.10) If $5(2x - 3) = 4x + 7$, what is x?

□ $x = 2$

□ $x = -5$

□ $x = 5$

□ $x = 11/3$

1.11) Solve for x: $6(x + 2) - 4 = 32$

□ $x = 5$

□ $x = 7$

□ $x = 4$

□ $x = 6$

1.12) Solve for y: $y/3 + 5 = 8$

□ $y = 12$

□ $y = 3$

□ $y = 6$

□ $y = 9$

1.13) If $3x + 4y = 12$ and $y = 2$, what is the value of x?

□ $x = 4$

□ $x = 2$

□ $x = 1$

□ $x = 4/3$

1.14) Solve for x: $2x - 3(2 - x) = 19$

□ $x = -1$

□ $x = 1$

□ $x = 3$

□ $x = 5$

1.15) Solve the equation: $x/2 - 4 = 3x/4 + 5$

□ $x = 18$

□ $x = -18$

□ $x = -36$

□ $x = 36$

1.16) Solve for x: $5(3x - 7) = 2(4x + 3)$

□ $x = 15$

□ $x = 17$

□ $x = 31$

□ $x = 41/7$

1.17) What is the solution to the equation: $2x + 5 = 5x - 10$

□ x = 10

□ x = 5

□ x = 15

□ x = -5

1.18) Solve for x: $4(x + 1) = 3(x + 3) - 3$

□ x = 6

□ x = 2

□ x = 4

□ x = 0

1.19) Solve the equation: $(x - 5)/3 = (x + 1)/4$

□ x = 20

□ x = 13

□ x = 23

□ x = 17

1.20) If $4(x - 5) = 2x + 6$, what is x?

□ x = 13

□ x = 9

□ x = 8

□ x = 11

1.21) Solve for x: $7x - 9 = 3x + 15$

- □ x = 3
- □ x = 24
- □ x = 12
- □ x = 6

1.22) Solve for y: $4y + 6 = 2(2y + 9)$

- □ y = 12
- □ y = 9
- □ y = 6
- □ No Solution

1.23) If $5x - 2y = 4$ and $x = 3$, what is the value of y?

- □ y = 3
- □ y = 7
- □ y = 1
- □ y = 5.5

1.24) Solve for x: $x + 4 = 2(x - 6) + 20$

- □ x = -4
- □ x = 8
- □ x = -8
- □ x = 4

1.25) Solve the equation: $3(x/4 - 2) = x - 9$

□ x = 16

□ x = 12

□ x = 4

□ x = 8

1.26) Solve for x: $6x + 5(2 - x) = 3x + 8$

□ x = -1

□ x = 2

□ x = 1

□ x = -2

1.27) What is the solution to the equation: $4x - 5 = -x + 10$

□ x = -3

□ x = -5

□ x = 5

□ x = 3

1.28) Solve for x: $5(x - 3) + 10 = 0$

□ x = 2

□ x = -2

□ x = -1

□ x = 1

1.29) Solve the equation: $(2x + 4)/2 = (3x - 6)/3$

□ $x = -18$

□ $x = 18$

□ No Solution

□ $x = 6$

1.30) If $2(x + 5) = x + 11$, what is x?

□ $x = -6$

□ $x = 6$

□ $x = -1$

□ $x = 1$

1.31) Solve for x: $x - 3 = 2x + 7$

□ $x = -5$

□ $x = 10$

□ $x = 5$

□ $x = -10$

1.32) Solve for y: $7y - 2(3y - 4) = 18$

□ $y = 4$

□ $y = 8$

□ $y = 10$

□ $y = 6$

1.33) If $2x + 3y = 21$ and $y = 3$, what is the value of x?

□ $x = 8$

□ $x = 7$

□ $x = 6$

□ $x = 5$

1.34) Solve for x: $3x + 5(1 - 2x) = x - 19$

□ $x = 5$

□ $x = 3$

□ $x = -5$

□ $x = -3$

1.35) Solve the equation: $(x/3) + 2 = (2x/6) - 1$

□ No Solution

□ $x = 12$

□ $x = -12$

□ $x = -6$

1.36) Solve for x: $4(2x - 3) = 3(3x + 2)$

□ $x = 2$

□ $x = 1$

□ $x = -18$

□ $x = -1$

1.37) What is the solution to the equation: $3x + 4 = 4x - 1$

□ x = 1

□ x = 5

□ x = -1

□ x = -5

1.38) Solve for x: $2(x + 6) - 3x = 12$

□ x = 6

□ x = -6

□ x = 12

□ x = 0

1.39) Solve the equation: $3(x - 4)/2 = (2x + 1)/3$

□ x = -15

□ x = 38/5

□ x = -10

□ x = 10

1.40) If $5(x + 3) = 3x + 15$, what is x?

□ x = 6

□ x = 0

□ x = 3

□ x = -3

Topic 1 - Answers

Question Number	Answer	Explanation
1.1	x = 5	Subtract 5 from both sides and divide by 3.
1.2	y = 6	Distribute 2, subtract 4 from both sides, add 6 and divide by 2.
1.3	x = 4	Subtract 2x from both sides and add 2.
1.4	x = 16	Multiply both sides by 2 and subtract 14.
1.5	x = 4.3	Distribute -1 through (2x + 3), combine like terms and solve.
1.6	x = 5	Distribute 3, combine like terms, and solve for x.
1.7	x = 18	Multiply both sides by 3 and add 6.
1.8	x = 11	Distribute 5 and 3, combine like terms, and solve for x.
1.9	x = -13	Distribute 2, subtract x from both sides, and subtract 5.
1.10	x = 11/3	Distribute 5, combine like terms, and solve for x.
1.11	x = 4	Distribute 6, add 4 to both sides, and solve for x.
1.12	y = 9	Multiply both sides by 3 and subtract 15.
1.13	x = 4/3	Substitute y with 2 into the equation and solve for x.
1.14	x = 5	Distribute -3, combine like terms, and solve for x.
1.15	x = -36	Find a common denominator, combine like terms, and solve.
1.16	x = 41/7	Distribute 5 and 2, combine like terms, and solve for x.
1.17	x = 5	Subtract 2x from both sides and add 10.
1.18	x = 2	Distribute 4 and solve.

1.19	x = 23	Find a common denominator, combine like terms, and solve.
1.20	x = 13	Distribute 4, subtract 2x from both sides, and solve for x.
1.21	x = 6	Subtract 3x from both sides and add 9.
1.22	No solution	No values of y work for this equation.
1.23	y = 5.5	Substitute x with 3 into the equation and solve for y.
1.24	x = -4	Distribute -2, combine like terms, and solve for x.
1.25	x = 12	Distribute 3, find a common denominator, combine like terms, and solve.
1.26	x = 1	Distribute 6 and 5, combine like terms, and solve for x.
1.27	x = 3	Add x to both sides and add 5.
1.28	x = 1	Distribute 5, subtract 10 from both sides, and solve for x.
1.29	No Solution	There are no values of x which make this equation work.
1.30	x = 1	Distribute 2, subtract x from both sides, and subtract 10.
1.31	x = -10	Subtract x from both sides and add 3.
1.32	y = 10	Distribute and solve for y.
1.33	x = 6	Substitute y with 3 into the equation and solve for x.
1.34	x = 3	Distribute 5, combine like terms, and solve for x.
1.35	No Solution	There are no values of x that make this equation work.
1.36	x = -18	Distribute 4 and 3, combine like terms, and solve for x.
1.37	x = 5	Subtract 3x from both sides and add 1.
1.38	x = 0	Distribute 2, combine like terms, and solve for x.
1.39	x = 38/5	Find a common denominator, combine like terms, and solve.
1.40	x = 0	Distribute 5, combine like terms, and solve for x.

Topic 2 – Transformations

2.1) What is a translation in geometry?

□ A slide in a straight line

□ An increase in size

□ A turn around a point

□ A flip over a line

2.2) Which transformation would you use to create a mirror image of a shape?

□ Translation

□ Dilation

□ Reflection

□ Rotation

2.3) If you rotate a figure 90 degrees clockwise, what type of transformation is it?

□ Rotation

□ Reflection

□ Translation

□ Dilation

2.4) Two figures are congruent if:

□ They are similar

□ They are of different sizes

□ They have the same shape and size

□ One is a mirror image of the other

2.5) When a shape is enlarged by a scale factor of 2, the transformation is called:

□ Translation

□ Rotation

□ Reflection

□ Dilation

2.6) Similar figures have:

□ The same size and shape

□ Corresponding angles that are different

□ The same shape but different sizes

□ Different shapes and sizes

2.7) The perimeters of two similar triangles are in the ratio 3:4. If one triangle has a perimeter of 21 units, what is the perimeter of the other?

□ 16 units

□ 14 units

□ 28 units

□ 32 units

2.8) A figure is translated 4 units up and 3 units to the left. What is this type of transformation called?

□ Rotation

□ Reflection

□ Translation

□ Dilation

2.9) What happens to the coordinates of a point (x, y) after a reflection over the y-axis?

□ (-x, y)

□ (y, x)

□ (x, -y)

□ (-y, -x)

2.10) If two shapes are similar and the scale factor is 1/2, how does the area of the smaller shape compare to the larger shape?

□ It is half as large

□ It is four times smaller

□ It is the same

□ It is twice as large

2.11) What is the result of a reflection of a point over the x-axis if the original point is (3, 5)?

□ (-3, -5)

□ (-3, 5)

□ (3, -5)

□ (3, 5)

2.12) Which transformation will change the size of a geometric figure?

□ Reflection

□ Translation

□ Dilation

□ Rotation

2.13) A figure is dilated with a scale factor of 2. What happens to the area of the figure?

□ It doubles

□ It is halved

□ It stays the same

□ It quadruples

2.14) What is true about the angles of a figure after a translation?

□ They double

□ They halve

□ They become zero

□ They remain the same

2.15) If two figures are similar and one is a dilation of the other with a scale factor of 3, what is the ratio of their corresponding side lengths?

□ 4:1

□ 1:9

□ 9:1

□ 1:3

2.16) Which of the following transformations can change a figure's orientation?

□ Dilation

□ Translation

□ Rotation

□ Reflection

2.17) When a figure is rotated 90 degrees counterclockwise, which of the following is true about a point (x, y)?

□ It becomes (-x, -y)

□ It becomes (x, y)

□ It becomes (y, -x)

□ It becomes (-y, x)

2.18) Two triangles are similar. If the first triangle has a side length of 5 and the second has a side length of 10, what is the scale factor?

□ 4:1

□ 1:2

□ 5:1

□ 1:4

2.19) A rectangle has its length increased by a factor of 2 and width increased by a factor of 3 through dilation. By what factor does the area increase?

□ 3

□ 6

□ 5

□ 2

2.20) A shape is translated according to the vector <5, -2>. Which way does the shape move?

□ 5 units left and 2 units up

□ 5 units right and 2 units down

□ 5 units left and 2 units down

□ 5 units right and 2 units up

2.21) A shape is rotated 180 degrees about the origin. What happens to its coordinates?

□ The coordinates of the shape are doubled.

□ The coordinates of the shape are negated.

□ The x-coordinates are negated, but the y-coordinates remain the same.

□ The shape's coordinates remain the same.

2.22) What is the result of a dilation with a scale factor of 0.5 on the area of a shape?

□ The area of the shape is reduced by half.

□ The area of the shape is reduced to a quarter.

□ The area of the shape remains unchanged.

□ The area of the shape is doubled.

2.23) If a square has a side length of 4 units before dilation and 6 units after dilation, what is the scale factor?

□ 0.66

□ 0.75

□ 1.5

□ 2

2.24) What is the result of reflecting a point over the line y = x?

□ The y-coordinate is negated, and the x-coordinate remains the same.

□ The x and y coordinates of the point are swapped.

□ The x and y coordinates of the point are negated.

□ The x-coordinate is negated, and the y-coordinate remains the same.

2.25) Which transformation changes the size of a geometric figure but not its shape?

□ Translation

□ Rotation

□ Dilation

□ Reflection

2.26) What happens to the coordinates of a point after a 90-degree rotation counterclockwise about the origin?

□ The coordinates are swapped.

□ The coordinates remain the same.

□ The x-coordinate becomes the y-coordinate, and the y-coordinate becomes the negative x-coordinate.

□ The x-coordinate becomes the negative y-coordinate, and the y-coordinate becomes the x-coordinate.

2.27) How are the perimeters of similar figures related?

□ The perimeters are unrelated.

□ The perimeters are proportional to the scale factor.

□ The perimeters are equal.

□ The perimeters are the same regardless of the scale factor.

2.28) If two figures are congruent, what can be said about their corresponding sides and angles?

□ The corresponding angles are proportional, and the sides are equal.

□ The corresponding sides and angles are equal.

□ The corresponding sides and angles are unrelated.

□ The corresponding sides are proportional, and the angles are equal.

2.29) A rectangle is translated 3 units right and 4 units down. How do you describe this movement vector?

□ The movement vector is <3, 4>.

□ The movement vector is <3, -4>.

□ The movement vector is <-3, -4>.

□ The movement vector is <-3, 4>.

2.30) What is the result of reflecting a shape across the y-axis?

□ The shape is rotated 180 degrees.

□ The x-coordinate of each point of the shape is negated.

□ Both the x and y coordinates of each point of the shape are negated.

□ The y-coordinate of each point of the shape is negated.

2.31) What is the effect on the coordinates of a point after a translation by the vector <3, -5>?

□ Both the x and y-coordinates decrease by 3 and increase by 5, respectively.

□ Both the x and y-coordinates increase by 3 and decrease by 5, respectively.

□ The x-coordinate increases by 3, and the y-coordinate decreases by 5.

□ The x-coordinate decreases by 3, and the y-coordinate increases by 5.

2.32) How do the angles of a figure change after a reflection over the line x = y?

□ The angles are halved.

□ The angles remain the same.

□ The angles are negated.

□ The angles are doubled.

2.33) If a parallelogram is rotated around its center by 180 degrees, what will be its position relative to its original position?

□ It will be upside down relative to its original position.

□ It will be in the same position.

□ It will be at a right angle to its original position.

□ It will be flipped over one of its diagonals.

2.34) When two triangles are congruent, what is true about their corresponding sides?

□ The corresponding sides are equal in length.

□ The corresponding sides are of different lengths.

□ The corresponding sides are in proportion to each other.

□ The corresponding sides are only equal if the triangles are also similar.

2.35) What is the relationship between the side lengths of similar figures?

□ The side lengths of similar figures are proportional.

□ The side lengths of similar figures are inversely proportional.

□ The side lengths of similar figures are equal.

□ The side lengths of similar figures are unrelated.

2.36) After a shape is dilated with a scale factor of 3, what happens to its perimeter?

□ The perimeter is nine times the original perimeter.

□ The perimeter is halved.

□ The perimeter remains the same.

□ The perimeter is tripled.

2.37) What transformation is performed if a shape is resized without altering its proportions?

□ Translation

□ Reflection

□ Rotation

□ Dilation

2.38) If two figures have the same shape but are not the same size, they are considered to be:

□ Congruent

□ Asymmetric

□ Equivalent

□ Similar

2.39) What does it mean for two polygons to be congruent?

□ They have the same size and shape.

□ They have the same number of sides.

□ They have the same perimeter.

□ They have the same area.

2.40) What is the result of reflecting a shape in the x-axis?

□ The figure returns to its original position.

□ The figure is rotated to a position perpendicular to its original position.

□ The figure's x and y coordinates are swapped.

□ The figure is turned upside down.

Topic 2 - Answers

Question Number	Answer	Explanation
2.1	A slide in a straight line	Translation moves a figure in a straight line without rotation.
2.2	Reflection	A mirror image is created by a reflection over a line.
2.3	Rotation	A 90-degree clockwise turn is a rotation.
2.4	They have the same shape and size	Congruent figures are identical in shape and size.
2.5	Dilation	Enlarging a shape by a scale factor is dilation.
2.6	The same shape but different sizes	Similar figures have proportional dimensions but are not identical in size.
2.7	28 units	The perimeters of similar figures are proportional to their scale factor. Since the ratio is 3:4, if one perimeter is 21 (a multiple of 3), the other is 28 (the same multiple of 4).
2.8	Translation	Moving a figure without rotation is translation.
2.9	(-x, y)	Reflection over the y-axis negates the x-coordinate.
2.10	It is four times smaller	The area is proportional to the square of the scale factor; since the scale factor is 1/2, the area is (1/2)^2 = 1/4 of the larger shape.
2.11	(3, -5)	Reflection over the x-axis negates the y-coordinate.
2.12	Dilation	Dilation changes the size.
2.13	It quadruples	Area scales by the square of the scale factor. If the scale factor is 2, the area is 2^2 = 4 times the original.
2.14	They remain the same	Translation does not affect angles.
2.15	1:3	The ratio of side lengths is the inverse of the scale factor. Since the scale factor is 3, the ratio of the smaller to the larger is 1:3.
2.16	Reflection	Orientation is the order of the labelling, reflection swaps that order
2.17	(-y, x)	A 90-degree counterclockwise rotation swaps the coordinates and negates the original x-coordinate.
2.18	1:2	The scale factor is the ratio of corresponding side lengths. Since one side is twice the other, the scale factor is 2:1.

2.19	6	Area increases by the product of the scale factors for length and width. If length is doubled (factor of 2) and width is tripled (factor of 3), the area increases by a factor of 2 x 3 = 6.
2.20	5 units right and 2 units down	A positive x-value in the vector indicates a rightward move; a negative y-value indicates a downward move.
2.21	The coordinates of the shape are negated.	A 180-degree rotation negates both coordinates.
2.22	The area of the shape is reduced to a quarter.	Area changes by the square of the scale factor. Since the scale factor is 0.5, the area is (0.5)^2 = 0.25 times the original, which is a quarter.
2.23	1.5	The new side length is 1.5 times the original side length.
2.24	The x and y coordinates of the point are swapped.	Reflecting over y = x swaps the coordinates.
2.25	Dilation	Dilation changes size but not shape.
2.26	The x-coordinate becomes the negative y-coordinate, and the y-coordinate becomes the x-coordinate.	This is the rule for 90-degree counterclockwise rotation.
2.27	The perimeters are proportional to the scale factor.	Similar figures have proportional perimeters.
2.28	The corresponding sides and angles are equal.	Congruent figures are identical in all aspects.
2.29	The movement vector is <3, -4>.	Rightward and downward moves are positive and negative, respectively.
2.30	The x-coordinate of each point of the shape is negated.	Reflection across the y-axis negates the x-coordinate.
2.31	The x-coordinate increases by 3, and the y-coordinate decreases by 5.	This is the effect of the translation vector <3, -5>.
2.32	The angles remain the same.	Reflection preserves the size and shape of figures, including angles.
2.33	It will be upside down relative to its original position.	A 180-degree rotation inverts the figure.

2.34	The corresponding sides are equal in length.	Congruency means all corresponding measurements are equal.
2.35	The side lengths of similar figures are proportional.	Similar figures have proportional dimensions.
2.36	The perimeter is tripled.	The perimeter changes linearly with the scale factor.
2.37	Dilation	Dilation resizes without altering proportions.
2.38	Similar	Similar figures have the same shape but different sizes.
2.39	They have the same size and shape.	Congruent figures are identical in all aspects.
2.40	The figure is turned upside down.	A 270-degree clockwise rotation effectively rotates the figure 90 degrees counterclockwise from its original position, which turns it upside down.

Topic 3 – Angles and Triangles

3.1) What is the value of each alternate interior angle if two parallel lines are cut by a transversal, and one of the alternate interior angles is 70°?

□ 100°

□ 110°

□ 70°

□ 80°

3.2) The sum of the angles of any triangle adds up to how many degrees?

□ 360°

□ 90°

□ 270°

□ 180°

3.3) In a triangle, if one angle measures 90 degrees and the second angle measures 45 degrees, what is the measure of the third angle?

□ 90°

□ 60°

□ 45°

□ 30°

3.4) A quadrilateral has how many degrees in its interior angles combined?

□ 180°

□ 90°

□ 270°

□ 360°

3.5) If two angles of one triangle are equal to two angles of another triangle, what can be said about the third pair of angles?

□ They are equal

□ They are complementary

□ No relation

□ They are supplementary

3.6) How many degrees are there in the sum of the interior angles of a pentagon?

□ 180°

□ 540°

□ 720°

□ 360°

3.7) If the two legs of a right triangle are equal in length, what are the measures of the angles besides the right angle?

□ 30° each

□ 45° each

□ 60° each

□ 30° and 60°

3.8) What is the sum of the interior angles of a hexagon?

□ 720°

□ 900°

□ 360°

□ 540°

3.9) If two triangles are similar, what can be said about their corresponding angles?

□ They are equal

□ They are complementary

□ They are proportional

□ They are supplementary

3.11) If two lines are cut by a transversal and the interior angles on the same side are supplementary, what can be said about the two lines?

□ They are perpendicular

□ They are not related

□ They are parallel

□ They intersect at a right angle

3.12) What is the measure of each interior angle of a regular pentagon (a five-sided polygon)?

□ 72°

□ 90°

□ 120°

□ 108°

3.13) If two alternate exterior angles are congruent, what can be inferred about the two lines crossed by the transversal?

□ They intersect at a 45° angle

□ They are parallel

□ They are perpendicular

□ They are not parallel

3.14) In a pair of similar triangles, the lengths of the sides of one are 5, 12, 13. If the shortest side of the other triangle is 10, what are the lengths of the other two sides?

□ 10, 13

□ 20, 26

□ 15, 18

□ 24, 26

3.15) What is the sum of the interior angles of an octagon (an eight-sided polygon)?

□ 900°

□ 1080°

□ 720°

□ 360°

3.16) What is the measure of an exterior angle of a regular hexagon (a six-sided polygon)?

□ 72°

□ 120°

□ 60°

□ 90°

3.17) If two corresponding angles are equal, what can be said about the two lines and the transversal?

□ The lines are coincident

□ The lines are perpendicular

□ The lines intersect at a 45° angle

□ The lines are parallel

3.18) When the exterior angles of a triangle are added together, what is their sum?

□ 270°

□ 360°

□ 180°

□ 90°

3.19) What is the ratio of the areas of two similar triangles with side length ratios of 1:3?

□ 1:2

□ 1:4

□ 1:6

□ 1:9

3.20) If a triangle has two sides of length 4 and 6, what is the length of the third side?

□ 5

□ Cannot be determined from the given information

□ √52

□ 10

3.21) What is the sum of the interior angles of a dodecagon (a twelve-sided polygon)?

□ 1800°

□ 1080°

□ 2160°

□ 1440°

3.22) If two parallel lines are cut by a transversal, what can be said about the corresponding angles?

□ They are not related

□ They are complementary

□ They are equal

□ They are supplementary

3.23) What is the measure of each exterior angle of a regular octagon?

□ 45°

□ 60°

□ 90°

□ 30°

3.24) How do you determine the number of diagonals in a polygon?

□ n(n - 4)/2, where n is the number of sides

□ n(n - 1)/2, where n is the number of sides

□ n(n - 3)/2, where n is the number of sides

□ n(n - 2)/2, where n is the number of sides

3.25) If the interior angles of a polygon are all congruent and each measures 120 degrees, how many sides does the polygon have?

□ 8

□ 5

□ 6

□ 7

3.26) In similar triangles, the ratio of their areas is equal to the square of the ratio of their corresponding sides. If the ratio of the sides is 2:3, what is the ratio of their areas?

□ 4:6

□ 2:3

□ 4:9

□ 6:9

3.27) If three parallel lines are cut by two transversals, what can be said about the segments formed on the transversals?

□ They are congruent

□ They are equal in length

□ They are proportional

□ No relation can be determined

3.28) When a transversal cuts two lines such that a pair of alternate exterior angles are congruent, which theorem or postulate can be used to prove the lines are parallel?

□ Corresponding Angles Postulate

□ Alternate Exterior Angles Theorem

□ Consecutive Interior Angles Theorem

□ Alternate Interior Angles Theorem

3.29) What is the measure of an interior angle of a regular heptagon (a seven-sided polygon)?

□ 135°

□ 120°

□ Approximately 128.57°

□ 130°

3.30) A triangle with sides of 5, 12, and 13 is placed next to a similar triangle with a side of 10. What is the length of the longest side of the second triangle?

□ 22

□ 20

□ 24

□ 26

3.31) In a 30-60-90 triangle, if the shortest side is 6, what are the lengths of the other two sides?

□ 6, $6\sqrt{2}$

□ $6\sqrt{3}$, 12

□ 12, 18

□ $6\sqrt{2}$, $6\sqrt{3}$

3.32) If a transversal intersects two lines and the interior angles on the same side of the transversal are supplementary, what is true about the lines?

□ The lines are parallel

□ The lines are not related

□ The lines are perpendicular

□ The lines intersect at a 45° angle

3.33) What is the measure of each interior angle of a regular decagon (a ten-sided polygon)?

□ 135°

□ 140°

□ 150°

□ 144°

3.34) How many diagonals does a nonagon (a nine-sided polygon) have?

□ 18

□ 27

□ 36

□ 45

3.35) What is the sum of the interior angles of a 15-sided polygon?

□ 1800°

□ 2520°

□ 2160°

□ 2340°

3.36) Which statement is true for the angles created when a transversal cuts two parallel lines?

□ All angles are acute

□ Consecutive interior angles are equal

□ Corresponding angles are supplementary

□ Alternate interior angles are equal

3.37) If two angles of a triangle are 65° and 45°, what is the measure of the third angle?

□ 80°

□ 75°

□ 70°

□ 85°

3.38) What is the measure of each exterior angle of a regular 12-sided polygon?

□ 30°

□ 40°

□ 25°

□ 35°

3.39) What is the scale factor between two similar triangles if the perimeters of the triangles are in the ratio 2:5?

□ 1:2

□ 2:5

□ 4:25

□ 2:3

3.40) If the ratio of the areas of two similar triangles is 4:9, what is the ratio of their corresponding heights?

□ 16:81

□ 8:27

□ 2:3

□ 4:9

Topic 3 - Answers

Question Number	Answer	Explanation
3.1	70°	Alternate interior angles formed by a transversal with parallel lines are equal.
3.2	180°	The sum of the angles in any triangle is 180 degrees.
3.3	45°	The third angle in a triangle can be found by subtracting the sum of the other two angles from 180 degrees.
3.4	360°	The sum of the interior angles of a quadrilateral is 360 degrees.
3.5	They are equal	If two angles of one triangle are equal to two angles of another triangle, by the Angle-Angle (AA) similarity postulate, the third angles are also equal.
3.6	540°	The sum of the interior angles of a pentagon can be calculated as $(n-2)\times180°$, where n is the number of sides.
3.7	45° each	In an isosceles right triangle, the two legs are congruent, and the non-right angles are both 45 degrees.
3.8	720°	The sum of the interior angles of a hexagon is 720 degrees.
3.9	They are equal	Corresponding angles in similar triangles are equal.
3.11	They are parallel	If the interior angles on the same side of a transversal are supplementary, the lines are parallel (converse of the same-side interior angles postulate).
3.12	108°	The measure of each interior angle of a regular pentagon can be calculated using the formula $(n-2)\times180°/n$, where n is the number of sides.
3.13	They are parallel	If two alternate exterior angles are congruent, the lines are parallel (converse of the alternate exterior angles theorem).
3.14	24, 26	In similar triangles, the lengths of corresponding sides are proportional. The ratio of similarity is 2:1.
3.15	1080°	The sum of the interior angles of an octagon is 1080 degrees.
3.16	60°	The measure of each exterior angle of a regular hexagon is 60 degrees.
3.17	The lines are parallel	If two corresponding angles are equal, the lines are parallel (converse of the corresponding angles postulate).
3.18	360°	The sum of the exterior angles of any triangle is 360 degrees.
3.19	1:9	The ratio of the areas of two similar triangles is the square of the ratio of their corresponding sides.

3.20	Cannot be determined from the given information	You cannot work out the third side of a triangle if you only know two other sides.
3.21	1800°	The sum of the interior angles of a dodecagon is 1800 degrees.
3.22	They are equal	Corresponding angles formed by a transversal with parallel lines are equal.
3.23	45°	The measure of each exterior angle of a regular octagon is 45 degrees.
3.24	n(n - 3)/2, where n is the number of sides	The number of diagonals in a polygon is given by the formula n(n - 3)/2.
3.25	6	If each interior angle measures 120 degrees, the polygon is a regular hexagon.
3.26	4:9	The ratio of the areas of two similar triangles is the square of the ratio of their corresponding sides.
3.27	They are proportional	The segments formed on the transversals are proportional (basic proportionality theorem).
3.28	Alternate Exterior Angles Theorem	This theorem can be used to prove the lines are parallel when alternate exterior angles are congruent.
3.29	Approximately 128.57°	The measure of an interior angle of a regular heptagon can be calculated using the formula (n-2)×180°/n.
3.30	26	In similar triangles, the lengths of corresponding sides are proportional.
3.31	6√3, 12	In a 30-60-90 triangle, the lengths of the sides opposite the angles are in the ratio 1:√3:2.
3.32	The lines are parallel	If a transversal intersects two lines and the interior angles on the same side are supplementary, the lines are parallel.
3.33	144°	The measure of each interior angle of a regular decagon is 144 degrees.
3.34	27	The number of diagonals in a nonagon can be calculated with the formula n(n - 3)/2.
3.35	2340°	The sum of the interior angles of a 15-sided polygon is 2340 degrees.
3.36	Alternate interior angles are equal	When a transversal cuts two parallel lines, alternate interior angles are equal.
3.37	70°	The sum of the angles in any triangle is 180 degrees. Subtracting the given angles gives the measure of the third angle.
3.38	30°	The measure of each exterior angle of a regular 12-sided polygon is 30 degrees.

3.39	2:5	The scale factor between two similar triangles is the same as the ratio of their perimeters.
3.40	2:3	The ratio of corresponding heights in two similar triangles is the same as the ratio of their corresponding sides.

Topic 4 - Linear Equations

4.1) What is the slope-intercept form of a linear equation?

□ x = my + b

□ y = mx + b

□ y = b + mx

□ y = mx - b

4.2) If a line passes through the points (2, 3) and (4, 7), what is the slope of the line?

□ 0.5

□ 2

□ 1.5

□ 3

4.3) How do you write an equation for a line with a slope of 1/2 and passing through the point (4, -1)?

□ y = 2x + 3

□ y = 1/2x - 3

□ y = 1/2x + 2

□ y = -1/2x - 3

4.4) What is the slope of a line that is parallel to the line $y = 3x + 4$?

□ 3

□ -3

□ -1/3

□ 4

4.5) What is the standard form of a linear equation?

□ $Ax + By = C$

□ $A(x + y) = C$

□ $Ax + By + C = 0$

□ $y = mx + b$

4.6) How is the slope of a vertical line defined?

□ Infinite

□ 0

□ 1

□ Undefined

4.7) What is the equation of a line that passes through the origin and has a slope of -2?

□ $y = 2x$

□ $x = -2y$

□ $y = -2x$

□ $y = -1/2x$

4.8) What is the slope of the line represented by the equation 2x - 3y = 6?

□ 2/3

□ -2/3

□ 3/2

□ -3/2

4.9) If a line has a slope of 0, what type of line is it?

□ Horizontal

□ Diagonal

□ Undefined

□ Vertical

4.10) What is the y-intercept of the line represented by the equation y = -4x + 2?

□ 2

□ 0

□ -4

□ -2

4.11) What is the slope of a line that is perpendicular to the line y = -2x + 3?

□ 2

□ 1/2

□ -1/2

□ -2

4.12) How do you find the slope of a line given the points (1, -2) and (3, 2)?

□ 1

□ -1

□ -2

□ 2

4.13) Write the equation of a line in slope-intercept form with a slope of 3 and passing through the point (0, -4).

□ y = 3x - 4

□ y = 3x + 4

□ y = -3x - 4

□ y = -3x + 4

4.14) If the graph of a linear equation passes through the points (5, 10) and (10, 20), what is the y-intercept?

□ 15

□ 5

□ 10

□ 0

4.15) Convert the equation 4y - 12x = 16 to slope-intercept form.

□ y = 3x - 4

□ y = -3x + 4

□ y = 3x + 4

□ y = -3x - 4

4.16) What is the slope of a horizontal line?

□ Undefined

□ 1

□ 0

□ -1

4.17) Write the equation of a line that has an undefined slope and passes through the point (7, -3).

□ x = 7

□ y = -3

□ x = -3

□ y = 7

4.18) What is the equation of the line in standard form that has a slope of -2 and y-intercept of 5?

□ $-2x - y = 5$

□ $-2x + y = 5$

□ $2x - y = 5$

□ $2x + y = 5$

4.19) If a line has an equation of $y = 5x + 10$, what is its slope?

□ -5

□ 10

□ 5

□ 1/5

4.20) What is the y-intercept of a line whose equation is $3x - 6y = 9$?

□ -1/2

□ 3

□ -3

□ -3/2

4.21) What is the slope of the line represented by the equation $5x - 2y = 10$?

□ 2/5

□ -2/5

□ 5/2

□ -5/2

4.22) If a line passes through the points (-1, 2) and (2, -1), what is the equation of the line in slope-intercept form?

□ $y = -x + 1$

□ $y = x - 1$

□ $y = x + 3$

□ $y = -x - 3$

4.23) Convert the equation $y = -3x + 6$ into standard form.

□ $-3x + y = 6$

□ $-3x - y = 6$

□ $3x - y = 6$

□ $3x + y = 6$

4.24) How do you write an equation for a line that is perpendicular to $y = 4x - 7$ and passes through the point (2, 3)?

□ $y = 1/4x + 3$

□ $y = -1/4x + 3.5$

□ $y = -1/4x - 3$

□ $y = 4x + 3$

4.25) What is the y-intercept of the line with equation $3x + 4y = 12$?

□ -3

□ 3

□ 0

□ 4

4.26) If the graph of a linear equation passes through (0, -4) and has a slope of 2, what is the equation of the line?

□ y = 2x + 4

□ y = -2x - 4

□ y = 2x - 4

□ y = -2x + 4

4.27) What is the slope of a line perpendicular to the line represented by the equation x + 4y = 8?

□ -1/4

□ 4

□ 1/4

□ -4

4.28) Write the equation of a line in standard form with a slope of -3 passing through the point (-2, 5).

□ 3x + y = 1

□ -3x + y = -11

□ -3x - y = 1

□ 3x - y = 11

4.29) What is the slope-intercept form of the equation 2y = 4x + 6?

□ y = 2x - 3

□ y = 4x + 3

□ y = 2x + 3

□ y = -2x + 3

4.30) If a line is defined by the equation y = -1/2x + 4, what is its slope?

□ 1/2

□ -2

□ -1/2

□ 2

4.31) Convert the linear equation 7y - 3x = 21 into slope-intercept form.

□ y = -3/7x - 3

□ y = 3/7x - 3

□ y = 3/7x + 3

□ y = -3/7x + 3

4.32) If a line has a y-intercept of -2 and a slope of 4, what is the equation of the line?

□ y = 4x + 2

□ y = 4x - 2

□ y = -4x - 2

□ y = -4x + 2

4.33) What is the slope of the line represented by the equation x - 5y = 10?

□ -5

□ 5

□ -1/5

□ 1/5

4.34) How do you write an equation for a line that passes through the point (3, -2) and has a slope of -1?

□ y = -x + 1

□ y = x + 1

□ y = x - 1

□ y = -x - 1

4.35) What is the equation of a line in slope-intercept form that is parallel to y = -2x + 3 and passes through the point (4, 5)?

□ y = -2x + 13

□ y = -2x + 11

□ y = 2x + 13

□ y = 2x + 3

4.36) If the graph of a linear equation has an x-intercept of 4 and a y-intercept of -3, what is the equation of the line?

□ y = 3/4x - 3

□ y = -4/3x + 4

□ y = -3/4x + 3

□ y = 4/3x - 4

4.37) What is the standard form of the equation of a line that has a slope of 1/2 and passes through the point (-4, 2)?

□ 2x + y = 8

□ x - 2y = -8

□ 2x - y = 8

□ x + 2y = -8

4.38) If a line has a slope of 3 and passes through the origin, what is its equation?

□ y = 3x + 3

□ y = -3x

□ y = 3x

□ y = -3x - 3

4.39) Convert the equation $2x + 3y = 6$ into slope-intercept form.

□ y = 2/3x + 2

□ y = -2/3x - 2

□ y = -2/3x + 2

□ y = 2/3x - 2

4.40) What is the y-intercept of a line whose equation is $y = 5x - 7$?

□ 5

□ 7

□ -7

□ 0

Topic 4 - Answers

Question Number	Answer	Explanation
4.1	y = mx + b	The slope-intercept form of a linear equation is y = mx + b, where m is the slope and b is the y-intercept.
4.2	2	The slope (m) is calculated by the change in y over the change in x (rise over run), so m = (7 - 3) / (4 - 2) = 4/2 = 2.
4.3	y = 1/2x - 3	Using the point-slope form, y - y1 = m(x - x1), and the point (4, -1), we get y + 1 = 1/2(x - 4), which simplifies to y = 1/2x - 3.
4.4	3	Lines that are parallel have the same slope. Therefore, the slope is 3.
4.5	Ax + By = C	The standard form of a linear equation is Ax + By = C, where A, B, and C are integers, and A is non-negative.
4.6	Undefined	The slope of a vertical line is undefined because the run (change in x) is 0, which would cause division by zero.
4.7	y = -2x	If a line passes through the origin, its y-intercept is 0. So the equation is y = -2x.
4.8	2/3	To find the slope from the standard form, we solve for y: 2x - 3y = 6 becomes y = 2/3x - 2, so the slope m is 2/3.
4.9	Horizontal	A line with a slope of 0 is horizontal.
4.10	2	The y-intercept of the line is the value of y when x = 0, which is 2.
4.11	1/2	A line perpendicular to another has a slope that is the negative reciprocal. So, the slope of the perpendicular line is 1/2.
4.12	2	Using the slope formula (y2 - y1) / (x2 - x1) for points (1, -2) and (3, 2), we get (2 - (-2)) / (3 - 1) = 4/2 = 2.
4.13	y = 3x - 4	Since the line passes through the origin (0, -4), the y-intercept is -4 and the slope is 3, thus y = 3x - 4.
4.14	0	Both given points lie on the line, and the y-intercept occurs where x = 0. Using the slope formula, the line has a slope of 2 and passes through (0, 0), thus the y-intercept is 0.
4.15	y = 3x + 4	To convert to slope-intercept form, solve for y: 4y = 12x + 16 becomes y = 3x + 4.
4.16	0	The slope of a horizontal line is 0 because there is no change in y as x changes.
4.17	x = 7	A line with an undefined slope is vertical, so its equation is x = a constant. The line passes through (7, -3), so the equation is x = 7.
4.18	2x + y = 5	The standard form is Ax + By = C. With a slope of -2 and y-intercept of 5, we rearrange y = -2x + 5 to get 2x + y = 5.
4.19	5	The slope is the coefficient of x in the slope-intercept form, which is 5.

4.20	-3/2	To find the y-intercept, set x to 0 and solve for y: 0 - 6y = 9 becomes y = -3/2.
4.21	5/2	To find the slope from the standard form, we solve for y: 5x - 2y = 10 becomes y = 5/2x - 5, so the slope m is 5/2.
4.22	y = -x + 1	Using the slope formula and the point-slope form, we find the slope is -1 and the equation is y = -x + 1.
4.23	3x + y = 6	To convert to standard form, rearrange the equation and multiply by -1 to get A as positive: -3x + y = -6 becomes 3x + y = 6.
4.24	y = -1/4x + 3.5	The slope of the perpendicular line is the negative reciprocal of 4, which is -1/4. Using the point-slope form with point (2, 3) gives y = -1/4x + 3.5.
4.25	3	To find the y-intercept, set x to 0 in the equation 3x + 4y = 12, giving 4y = 12, so y = 3.
4.26	y = 2x - 4	Using the slope 2 and the y-intercept -4, the equation in slope-intercept form is y = 2x - 4.
4.27	4	The slope of a perpendicular line is the negative reciprocal, so for the line x + 4y = 8, the slope of the perpendicular line is 4.
4.28	3x + y = 1	Using the point-slope form with the slope -3 and point (-2, 5), we get y + 5 = -3(x + 2), which simplifies to 3x + y = 1.
4.29	y = 2x + 3	Divide the entire equation by 2 to solve for y in slope-intercept form: y = 2x + 3.
4.30	-1/2	The slope is the coefficient of x in the slope-intercept form, which is -1/2.
4.31	y = 3/7x + 3	To convert to slope-intercept form, divide each term by 7: y = 3/7x + 3.
4.32	y = 4x - 2	With a y-intercept of -2 and a slope of 4, the equation is y = 4x - 2.
4.33	1/5	To find the slope from the standard form, solve for y: x - 5y = 10 becomes y = 1/5x - 2, so the slope m is 1/5.
4.34	y = -x + 1	Using the point-slope form with the slope -1 and point (3, -2), we get y + 2 = -1(x - 3), which simplifies to y = -x + 1.
4.35	y = -2x + 13	To find a line parallel to y = -2x + 3, use the same slope -2. With point (4, 5), the equation is y = -2x + 13.
4.36	y = 3/4x - 3	To find the equation with x-intercept 4 and y-intercept -3, convert the intercept form x/a + y/b = 1 to slope-intercept form.
4.37	x - 2y = -8	Using the point-slope form with the slope 1/2 and point (-4, 2), we get y - 2 = 1/2(x + 4), which simplifies to x - 2y = -8.
4.38	y = 3x	A line passing through the origin with slope 3 has the equation y = 3x.
4.39	y = -2/3x + 2	To convert to slope-intercept form, divide each term by 3: y = -2/3x + 2.
4.40	-7	The y-intercept of the line is the value of y when x = 0, which is -7.

Topic 5 - Systems of Linear Equations

5.1) What is the graphical representation of a system of linear equations that has one solution?

□ Two intersecting lines

□ Two parallel lines

□ A single line

□ Two overlapping lines

5.2) How can you determine the solution of a system of linear equations using substitution?

□ Solve one equation for one variable and substitute into the other equation

□ Graph the equations on the same axes

□ Multiply one equation by the other

□ Add the equations together

5.3) What is the result of a system of linear equations if the lines are parallel and distinct?

□ One solution

□ Two solutions

□ No solution

□ Infinite solutions

5.4) Describe the solution set for a system of linear equations represented by the same line.

□ Exactly two solutions

□ One solution

□ Infinite solutions

□ No solution

5.5) When using elimination to solve a system of equations, what is the first step if the coefficients of one variable are not opposites?

□ Add the equations as they are

□ Substitute one variable

□ Graph the equations

□ Multiply one or both equations by a number to get opposite coefficients

5.6) What does it mean for a system of linear equations to be consistent?

□ The system's equations are identical

□ The system has at least one solution

□ The system has no solution

□ The system has exactly two solutions

5.7) How do you write the solution for a system of linear equations that has an infinite number of solutions?

□ No solution

□ As an equation or a set of parametric equations

□ As a single value

□ With a single ordered pair

5.8) What is the solution to the system of equations $y = 2x + 1$ and $y = 2x - 3$?

□ (1, 3)

□ No solution

□ (2, 5)

□ Infinite solutions

5.9) If you solve a system of equations and get the statement $4 = 4$, what can you conclude?

□ The system has infinite solutions

□ The system has one solution

□ The system has no solution

□ The equations are not a system

5.10) What method can you use to solve a system of equations if the coefficients of one of the variables are already opposites?

□ Matrix method

□ Substitution

□ Graphical

□ Elimination

5.11) What is the solution to the system of equations $2x + 3y = 12$ and $2x + y = 8$?

□ $x = 2, y = 3$

□ Infinite solutions

□ $x = 3, y = 2$

□ $x = 2, y = 3$

5.12) What is the solution to the system of equations $3x + 3y = 18$ and $5x + 3y = 28$?

□ $x = 1, y = 5$

□ $x = 5, y = 1$

□ $x = 5, y = 1$

□ No solution

5.13) What is the solution to the system of equations $4x - y = 8$ and $6x + y = 22$?

□ $x = 3, y = 4$

□ $x = 3, y = 5$

□ No solution

□ Infinite solutions

5.14) What is the solution to the system of equations $a + 2b = 5$ and $3a + 4b = 11$?

□ $a = 2, b = 1$

□ $a = 1, b = 2$

□ No solution

□ Infinite solutions

5.15) What is the solution to the system of equations $5a + b = 7$ and $8a - 2b = 4$?

□ No solution

□ $a = 1, b = 2$

□ $a = 2, b = 1$

□ Infinite solutions

5.16) Solve the simultaneous equations: $2x + 5y = 2$ and $2x + 3y = 2$

□ x = 2, y = 1

□ x = 1, y = 0

□ No solution

□ x = 3, y = 2

5.17) Solve the simultaneous equations: $3x + 4y = 23$ and $2x - 4y = 2$

□ x = 4, y = 1

□ x = 6, y = 3

□ No solution

□ x = 5, y = 2

5.18) Solve the simultaneous equations: $7x + 2y = 33$ and $4x + 2y = 24$

□ x = 2, y = 5

□ x = 4, y = 7

□ x = 3, y = 6

□ No solution

5.19) Solve the simultaneous equations: $x + y = 7$ and $2x + 5y = 8$

□ x = 2, y = -2

□ x = 9, y = -2

□ x = 4, y = 0

□ No solution

5.20) Solve the simultaneous equations: $3x + 2y = 17$ and $5x + -2y = 7$

□ x = 4, y = 5

□ No solution

□ x = 2, y = 3

□ x = 3, y = 4

5.21) Solve the simultaneous equations: $5x - 3y = 24$ and $3x + 2y = 3$

□ x = 3, y = -3

□ No solution

□ x = 2, y = -4

□ x = 4, y = -2

5.22) Solve the simultaneous equations: $6x + 7y = 11$ and $4x + 3y = 9$

□ No solution

□ x = 3, y = -1

□ x = 4, y = 0

□ x = 2, y = -2

5.23) Solve the simultaneous equations: $10x + 9y = 42$ and $5x - 3y = 36$

□ No solution

□ x = 5, y = -3

□ x = 4, y = -4

□ x = 6, y = -2

5.24) Which method of solving systems of linear equations involves making the coefficients of one variable equal and then adding or subtracting the equations?

□ Substitution

□ Elimination

□ Graphical method

□ Matrix method

5.25) If a system of linear equations has no solution, what does this imply about the graphs of the equations?

□ The lines overlap completely

□ The lines are parallel

□ The lines intersect at multiple points

□ The lines intersect at one point

5.26) When using the substitution method to solve a system of equations, what is a crucial first step?

□ Find the y-intercept of each equation

□ Eliminate one variable immediately

□ Graph both equations to find the intercepts

□ Solve one equation for one of its variables

5.27) In the context of linear equations, what does it mean for a system to be inconsistent?

□ It has exactly one solution

□ It has no solution

□ It has infinitely many solutions

□ It has exactly two solutions

5.28) What is the main advantage of using the elimination method over the substitution method in solving a system of linear equations?

□ It's faster when the equations are complex

□ It requires less algebraic manipulation

□ It always gives the exact solution in fewer steps

□ It's more visually intuitive

5.29) In a special system of linear equations, the two lines are identical. What can be said about the number of solutions to this system?

□ No solution

□ Exactly one solution

□ Exactly two solutions

□ Infinitely many solutions

5.30) What is the result of a system of linear equations if, upon solving, you get an identity, like 5 = 5?

□ Cannot be determined

□ One solution

□ No solution

□ Infinitely many solutions

5.31) What does the graphical method of solving a system of linear equations involve?

□ Drawing a straight line for each equation

□ Eliminating one variable

□ Substituting one equation into another

□ Using matrices to find the solution

5.32) If the equations in a system of linear equations represent the same line, this system is classified as:

□ Inconsistent

□ Consistent and independent

□ Non-linear

□ Consistent and dependent

5.33) What are the possible solutions for a system of linear equations where the lines are perpendicular?

□ Exactly one solution

□ No solution

□ Infinitely many solutions

□ Exactly two solutions

5.34) Solve the simultaneous equations: $2x + 5y = 2$ and $2x + 3y = 2$

□ $x = 2, y = 1$

□ $x = 1, y = 0$

□ No solution

□ Infinite solutions

5.35) Solve the simultaneous equations: $3x + 4y = 23$ and $2x - 4y = 2$

□ $x = 4, y = 3$

□ $x = 3, y = 4$

□ No solution

□ $x = 5, y = 2$

5.36) Solve the simultaneous equations: $7x + 2y = 33$ and $4x + 2y = 24$

□ $x = 3, y = 6$

□ No solution

□ $x = 9, y = 7$

□ $x = 15, y = 3$

5.37) Solve the simultaneous equations: $10x + y = 88$ and $7x + y = 61$

□ $x = 5, y = 5$

□ No solution

□ $x = 3, y = 9$

□ $x = 9, y = -2$

5.38) Solve the simultaneous equations: $3x + 2y = 17$ and $5x - 2y = 7$

□ $x = 5, y = 4$

□ $x = 3, y = 4$

□ No solution

□ $x = 4, y = 5$

5.39) Solve the simultaneous equations: $4x + 5y = 14$ and $4x - 3y = -2$

□ $x = 3, y = 0$

□ $x = 1, y = 2$

□ No solution

□ $x = 2, y = 1$

5.40) Solve the simultaneous equations: $3x + 5y = 29$ and $7x - 5y = 1$

□ $x = 5, y = 2$

□ $x = 4, y = 3$

□ $x = 3, y = 4$

□ No solution

Topic 5 - Answers

Question Number	Answer	Explanation
5.1	Two intersecting lines	A system with one solution means the graphs intersect at exactly one point.
5.2	Solve one equation for one variable and substitute into the other equation	In substitution, one equation is solved for one variable and then substituted into the other equation.
5.3	No solution	Parallel and distinct lines never intersect, indicating no solutions.
5.4	Infinite solutions	Identical lines (overlapping) represent the same equation, hence have infinite solutions.
5.5	Multiply one or both equations by a number to get opposite coefficients	This step prepares the equations for elimination of one variable.
5.6	The system has at least one solution	A consistent system means there is at least one solution.
5.7	As an equation or a set of parametric equations	Infinite solutions are expressed as an equation or parametric equations.
5.8	No solution	Parallel lines (same slope, different intercepts) do not intersect, hence no solution.
5.9	Infinitely many solutions	An identity (like 4=4) indicates the system is dependent with infinitely many solutions.
5.10	Elimination	If the coefficients are already opposites, elimination is the most straightforward method.
5.11	x = 3, y = 2	Solving the system yields this specific solution.
5.12	x = 5, y = 1	Solving the system yields this specific solution.
5.13	x = 3, y = 4	Solving the system yields this specific solution.
5.14	a = 1, b = 2	Solving the system yields this specific solution.
5.15	a = 1, b = 2	Solving the system yields this specific solution.
5.16	x = 1, y = 0	Solving the system yields this specific solution.
5.17	x = 5, y = 2	Solving the system yields this specific solution.
.18	x = 3, y = 6	Solving the system yields this specific solution.

5.19	x = 9, y = -2	Solving the system yields this specific solution.
5.20	x = 3, y = 4	Solving the system yields this specific solution.
5.21	x = 3, y = -3	Solving the system yields this specific solution.
5.22	x = 3, y = -1	Solving the system yields this specific solution.
5.23	x = 6, y = -2	Solving the system yields this specific solution.
5.24	Elimination	This method involves making coefficients of one variable equal for elimination.
5.25	The lines are parallel	No solution implies the lines are parallel and do not intersect.
5.26	Solve one equation for one of its variables	A crucial first step in substitution is to isolate one variable in one equation.
5.27	It has no solution	An inconsistent system does not have any solution.
5.28	It's faster when the equations are complex	Elimination can be quicker and less complex for solving some systems.
5.29	Infinitely many solutions	Identical lines indicate an infinite number of solutions.
5.30	Infinitely many solutions	An identity like 5 = 5 in a system suggests infinite solutions.
5.31	Drawing a straight line for each equation	The graphical method involves plotting each equation as a line on a graph.
5.32	Consistent and dependent	If equations represent the same line, the system is dependent with infinite solutions.
5.33	Exactly one solution	Perpendicular lines intersect at exactly one point, indicating a single solution.
5.34	x = 1, y = 0	Solving the system yields this specific solution.
5.35	x = 5, y = 2	Solving the system yields this specific solution.
5.36	x = 3, y = 6	Solving the system yields this specific solution.
5.37	x = 9, y = -2	Solving the system yields this specific solution.
5.38	x = 3, y = 4	Solving the system yields this specific solution.
5.39	x = 1, y = 2	Solving the system yields this specific solution.
5.40	x = 3, y = 4	Solving the system yields this specific solution.

Topic 6 - Functions

6.1) If f(x) = 6x + 4, what is f(3)?

□ 26

□ 14

□ 22

□ 18

6.2) What is the output of the function g(x) = 2x^2 when x = 4?

□ 32

□ 8

□ 16

□ 64

6.3) If h(x) = x/2 - 3, find h(10).

□ 5

□ -5

□ 1

□ 2

6.4) Given the function $f(x) = 3x - 5$, what is the value of x when $f(x) = 10$?

□ 15

□ 5

□ 10

□ 3

6.5) For the function $f(x) = x^2$, what is $f(-3)$?

□ 6

□ -9

□ -6

□ 9

6.6) What is the slope of the linear function represented by the equation $y = 5x + 2$?

□ 7

□ 5

□ 2

□ 10

6.7) If a function f is defined as $f(x) = x^3$, what is $f(2)$?

□ 10

□ 8

□ 4

□ 6

6.8) For the linear function $f(x) = 4x$, what is the y-intercept of its graph?

□ -4

□ 1

□ 0

□ 4

6.9) If a function is defined as $f(x) = 2x - 7$, what is the value of $f(-1)$?

□ 5

□ 9

□ -5

□ -9

6.10) What is the value of x in the function $f(x) = x^2 + 6x + 9$ when $f(x) = 0$?

□ 0

□ 3

□ -6

□ -3

6.11) If the function f is defined as $f(x) = x^2 - 4x + 4$, what is $f(5)$?

□ 16

□ 11

□ 25

□ 9

6.12) Describe the graph of the function $f(x) = x + 3$.

□ A horizontal line

□ A vertical line

□ A parabola opening upwards

□ A straight line with a slope of 1

6.13) What is the domain of the function $f(x) = 1/x$?

□ Only negative real numbers

□ Only positive real numbers

□ All real numbers except zero

□ All real numbers

6.14) If a function f is defined as $f(x) = 3x^2$, what is the rate of change of the function?

□ Constant

□ Proportional to x

□ Linearly increasing

□ Decreasing as x increases

6.15) Find the x-intercept of the function $f(x) = 2x - 6$.

□ 2

□ 6

□ 3

□ -3

6.16) What is the range of the function defined by f(x) = 4 - x^2?

□ All real numbers greater than or equal to -4

□ All real numbers less than or equal to 4

□ Only positive real numbers

□ All real numbers

6.17) If g(x) = x^3 and h(x) = 3x, what is (g + h)(2)?

□ 14

□ 8

□ 12

□ 10

6.18) How does the graph of f(x) = x^2 differ from the graph of g(x) = x^2 + 5?

□ g(x) is shifted 5 units down

□ g(x) is shifted 5 units up

□ g(x) is steeper

□ g(x) has a different curvature

6.19) What is the slope of the line represented by the equation y = -3x + 4?

□ -4

□ 3

□ -3

□ 4

6.20) A function is defined as $f(x) = 7$. What type of function is this?

□ Quadratic function

□ Linear function

□ Cubic function

□ Constant function

6.21) What is the output of the function $f(x) = 3x - 7$ when $x = -2$?

□ 1

□ 7

□ -1

□ -13

6.22) If $f(x) = x^2$ and $g(x) = x + 4$, find the value of $f(g(2))$.

□ 16

□ 8

□ 12

□ 36

6.23) Determine the value of the quadratic function $f(x) = x^2 - 6x + 8$ at $x = 0$.

□ 0

□ 2

□ 8

□ 4

6.24) If $f(x) = 1/(x - 2)$, what is the value of $f(5)$?

□ 3

□ 1/2

□ 2

□ 1/3

6.25) What type of function is represented by the equation $y = 2^x$?

□ Exponential function

□ Linear function

□ Logarithmic function

□ Quadratic function

6.26) Find the slope of the function $f(x) = -4x + 1$.

□ 4

□ -1

□ -4

□ 1

6.27) What is the range of the function $f(x) = \text{sqrt}(x)$?

□ All real numbers

□ Only positive real numbers

□ All real numbers less than 0

□ All real numbers greater than or equal to 0

6.28) If $f(x) = x^3 - 2x$ and $g(x) = 5x$, find the value of $(f - g)(2)$.

- □ -6
- □ -2
- □ 6
- □ 2

6.29) What is the inverse function of $f(x) = 3x + 2$?

- □ $(x - 2)/3$
- □ $(x + 2)/3$
- □ $3x - 2$
- □ $(3 - x)/2$

6.30) If the function h is defined as $h(x) = 4/x$, what is $h(1/2)$?

- □ 4
- □ 8
- □ 1/8
- □ 2

6.31) If the function f is defined as $f(x) = 2x^2 - 5$, what is $f(-3)$?

- □ 13
- □ 23
- □ -13
- □ -23

6.32) Describe the graph of the function f(x) = -x + 2.

□ A parabola opening upwards

□ A straight line with a negative slope

□ A straight line with a positive slope

□ A parabola opening downwards

6.33) What is the domain of the function f(x) = sqrt(x - 3)?

□ All real numbers greater than or equal to 3

□ All real numbers

□ Only positive real numbers

□ All real numbers less than 3

6.34) If f(x) = x^3, what is the value of the function at x = 2?

□ 8

□ 12

□ 4

□ 6

6.35) Find the y-intercept of the function f(x) = -3x + 6.

□ -3

□ 6

□ 3

□ -6

6.36) What is the range of the function defined by $f(x) = 1/(x^2)$?

□ All real numbers less than 0

□ All real numbers

□ All real numbers except 0

□ All real numbers greater than 0

6.37) If $g(x) = x^2$ and $h(x) = 2x$, what is $(g - h)(3)$?

□ 3

□ 6

□ 9

□ 12

6.38) How does the graph of $f(x) = (x - 2)^2$ differ from the graph of $g(x) = x^2$?

□ g(x) has a wider curvature

□ g(x) is shifted 2 units to the right

□ g(x) is shifted 2 units to the left

□ g(x) is steeper than f(x)

6.39) What is the slope of the line represented by the equation $y = 5x - 4$?

□ -5

□ 4

□ 5

□ -4

6.40) A function is defined as f(x) = x^4. Is this function even, odd, or neither?

□ Neither

□ Cannot be determined

□ Even

□ Odd

Topic 6 - Answers

Question Number	Answer	Explanation
6.1	22	f(3) = 6*3 + 4 = 18 + 4 = 22
6.2	32	g(4) = 24^2 = 216 = 32
6.3	2	h(10) = 10/2 - 3 = 5 - 3 = 2
6.4	5	Solving 3x - 5 = 10 gives x = 5
6.5	9	f(-3) = (-3)^2 = 9
6.6	5	The slope in y = 5x + 2 is 5
6.7	8	f(2) = 2^3 = 8
6.8	0	The y-intercept of f(x) = 4x is 0 (where x = 0)
6.9	-9	f(-1) = 2*(-1) - 7 = -2 - 7 = -9
6.10	-3	Solving x^2 + 6x + 9 = 0 gives x = -3
6.11	9	f(5) = 5^2 - 4*5 + 4 = 25 - 20 + 4 = 9
6.12	A straight line with a slope of 1	The graph of f(x) = x + 3 is a straight line with slope 1
6.13	All real numbers except zero	The domain of f(x) = 1/x excludes x = 0
6.14	Proportional to x	The rate of change of f(x) = 3x^2 varies with x
6.15	3	The x-intercept is found by setting f(x) = 0, giving x = 3
6.16	All real numbers less than or equal to 4	The range of f(x) = 4 - x^2 is all values ≤ 4
6.17	14	(g + h)(2) = g(2) + h(2) = 2^3 + 3*2 = 8 + 6 = 14

6.18	g(x) is shifted 5 units up	The graph of g(x) = x^2 + 5 is shifted up by 5 units compared to f(x) = x^2
6.19	-3	The slope in y = -3x + 4 is -3
6.20	Constant function	f(x) = 7 is a constant function as it always outputs 7
6.21	-13	f(-2) = 3*(-2) - 7 = -6 - 7 = -13
6.22	36	f(g(2)) = f(2 + 4) = f(6) = 6^2 = 36
6.23	8	Substitute x for 0, which gives you f(0) = 8
6.24	1/3	f(5) = 1/(5 - 2) = 1/3
6.25	Exponential function	y = 2^x is an exponential function
6.26	-4	The slope of f(x) = -4x + 1 is -4
6.27	All real numbers greater than or equal to 0	The range of f(x) = sqrt(x) includes all non-negative real numbers
6.28	6	(f - g)(2) = f(2) - g(2) = (2^3 - 22) - 52 = 8 - 4 - 10 = 6
6.29	(x - 2)/3	The inverse of f(x) = 3x + 2 is (x - 2)/3
6.30	8	h(1/2) = 4/(1/2) = 8
6.31	13	f(-3) = 2*(-3)^2 - 5 = 2*9 - 5 = 18 - 5 = 13
6.32	A straight line with a negative slope	The graph of f(x) = -x + 2 is a straight line with a negative slope
6.33	All real numbers greater than or equal to 3	The domain of f(x) = sqrt(x - 3) is x ≥ 3
6.34	8	Substitute x for 2 to give f(2) = 8
6.35	6	The y-intercept of f(x) = -3x + 6 is 6 (where x = 0)
6.36	All real numbers	The range of f(x) = 1/(x^2) includes all values > 0

	greater than 0	
6.37	3	(g - h)(3) = g(3) - h(3) = 3^2 - 2*3 = 9 - 6 = 3
6.38	g(x) is shifted 2 units to the right	The graph of f(x) = (x - 2)^2 is shifted 2 units right compared to g(x) = x^2
6.39	5	The slope in y = 5x - 4 is 5
6.40	Even	f(x) = x^4 is an even function as f(-x) = f(x)

Topic 7 - Exponents

7.1) If 2^4 is an example of an exponent, what does the 4 represent?

□ The exponent

□ The coefficient

□ The base

□ The product

7.2) What is the value of 3^3 * 3^2 using the product of powers property?

□ 3^5

□ 9

□ 3^6

□ 27

7.3) How is 5^0 defined?

□ 0

□ 5

□ Undefined

□ 1

7.4) What is the quotient of 7^5 / 7^2 using the quotient of powers property?

□ 14

□ 35

□ 7^3

□ 7^7

7.5) What does a negative exponent indicate, as in 4^-2?

□ Negative base

□ Zero

□ Reciprocal of the base raised to the positive exponent

□ Undefined

7.6) Express 300,000 in scientific notation.

□ 300 x 10^3

□ 0.3 x 10^6

□ 3 x 10^6

□ 3 x 10^5

7.7) If a number is written as 5.67 x 10^3 in scientific notation, what is its standard form?

□ 56700

□ 5670

□ 56.7

□ 5.67

7.8) Simplify the expression (2^3)^4 using the power of a power rule.

□ 2^7

□ 16

□ 2^12

□ 8^4

7.9) What is the result of multiplying 2 x 10^3 by 3 x 10^4?

□ 5 x 10^7

□ 6 x 10^7

□ 6 x 10^12

□ 6 x 10^8

7.10) How do you express 0.00045 in scientific notation?

□ 4.5 x 10^-5

□ 45 x 10^-5

□ 4.5 x 10^-4

□ 0.45 x 10^-3

7.11) What is the simplified form of 2^-3?

□ -8

□ -1/8

□ 1/8

□ 8

7.12) How do you express 0.000123 in scientific notation?

□ 1.23 x 10^-4

□ 12.3 x 10^-5

□ 123 x 10^-6

□ 0.123 x 10^-3

7.13) If a number is written as 4.5 x 10^-2 in scientific notation, what is its standard form?

□ 0.45

□ 0.045

□ 45

□ 0.0045

7.14) What is the result of dividing 4 x 10^6 by 2 x 10^2?

□ 20 x 10^5

□ 2 x 10^4

□ 20 x 10^4

□ 2 x 10^3

7.15) Simplify the expression (3^2)^3 using the power of a power rule.

□ 3^6

□ 9^3

□ 81

□ 27

7.16) What is the value of 10^0?

□ 1

□ 10

□ Undefined

□ 0

7.17) Express 0.0056 in scientific notation.

□ 5.6×10^{-4}

□ 5.6×10^{-3}

□ 0.56×10^{-2}

□ 56×10^{-4}

7.18) What is the simplified form of the expression $(5^4) / (5^2)$?

□ 5^2

□ 10

□ 5^6

□ 25

7.19) If $f(x) = 2^x$, what is $f(-2)$?

□ 1/4

□ 4

□ -4

□ -1/4

7.20) How is 7^1 * 7^-1 simplified?

□ 14

□ 1

□ 7

□ 0

7.21) What is the value of 5^2 * 5^3?

□ 125

□ 25

□ 5^5

□ 5^6

7.22) Express 700 in scientific notation.

□ 7 x 10^2

□ 7 x 10^3

□ 0.7 x 10^3

□ 70 x 10^1

7.23) If a number is written as 3.2 x 10^-3 in scientific notation, what is its standard form?

□ 0.00032

□ 0.032

□ 0.0032

□ 32

7.24) What is the result of multiplying 5×10^4 by 3×10^3?

□ 1.5×10^8

□ 15×10^7

□ 15×10^8

□ 1.5×10^7

7.25) Simplify the expression $(4^3)^2$ using the power of a power rule.

□ 256

□ 4^6

□ 16^2

□ 64

7.26) What is the value of 2^{-1}?

□ -1/2

□ 2

□ 1/2

□ -2

7.27) Express 0.000089 in scientific notation.

□ 8.9×10^{-4}

□ 0.89×10^{-4}

□ 89×10^{-6}

□ 8.9×10^{-5}

7.28) What is the simplified form of the expression (6^3) / (6^2)?

□ 18

□ 6^5

□ 36

□ 6

7.29) If f(x) = 3^x, what is f(-3)?

□ 1/27

□ -27

□ -1/27

□ 27

7.30) How is 9^1 * 9^-1 simplified?

□ 9

□ 81

□ 18

□ 1

7.31) What is the value of (2^3) * (2^4)?

□ 64

□ 2^12

□ 2^7

□ 16

7.32) Express 0.0025 in scientific notation.

□ 25 x 10^-4

□ 0.25 x 10^-2

□ 2.5 x 10^-4

□ 2.5 x 10^-3

7.33) If a number is written as 7.5 x 10^2 in scientific notation, what is its standard form?

□ 7500

□ 75

□ 750

□ 0.75

7.34) What is the result of dividing 8 x 10^5 by 4 x 10^2?

□ 2 x 10^3

□ 20 x 10^4

□ 2 x 10^7

□ 20 x 10^3

7.35) Simplify the expression (5^2)^3 using the power of a power rule.

□ 5^5

□ 125

□ 25^3

□ 5^6

7.36) What is the value of 3^-2?

□ -1/9

□ -9

□ 1/9

□ 9

7.37) Express 0.000007 in scientific notation.

□ 0.7 x 10^-5

□ 70 x 10^-7

□ 7 x 10^-6

□ 7 x 10^-7

7.38) What is the simplified form of the expression (8^4) / (8^2)?

□ 16

□ 8^2

□ 64

□ 8^6

7.39) If f(x) = 4^x, what is f(-4)?

□ 256

□ -256

□ 1/256

□ -1/256

7.40) How is 6^1 * 6^-1 simplified?

□ 6

□ 1

□ 12

□ 36

Topic 7 - Answers

Question Number	Answer	Explanation
7.1	The exponent	In 2^4, the 4 represents the exponent, indicating how many times the base (2) is multiplied by itself.
7.2	3^5	Using the product of powers property, $3^3 * 3^2$ equals $3^{(3+2)}$ or 3^5.
7.3	1	Any number raised to the power of 0 is 1.
7.4	7^3	Using the quotient of powers property, $7^5 / 7^2$ equals $7^{(5-2)}$ or 7^3.
7.5	Reciprocal of the base raised to the positive exponent	A negative exponent indicates the reciprocal of the base raised to the positive exponent.
7.6	3×10^5	300,000 in scientific notation is 3×10^5.
7.7	5670	5.67×10^3 in standard form is 5670.
7.8	2^{12}	$(2^3)^4$ is simplified using the power of a power rule to $2^{(3*4)}$ or 2^{12}.
7.9	6×10^7	Multiplying 2×10^3 by 3×10^4 gives $6 \times 10^{(3+4)}$ or 6×10^7.
7.10	4.5×10^{-5}	0.00045 in scientific notation is 4.5×10^{-5}.
7.11	1/8	2^{-3} is the reciprocal of 2^3, which is 1/8.
7.12	1.23×10^{-4}	0.000123 in scientific notation is 1.23×10^{-4}.
7.13	0.045	4.5×10^{-2} in standard form is 0.045.
7.14	2×10^4	Dividing 4×10^6 by 2×10^2 gives $2 \times 10^{(6-2)}$ or 2×10^4.
7.15	3^6	$(3^2)^3$ is simplified to $3^{(2*3)}$ or 3^6.
7.16	1	10^0 is always 1.
7.17	5.6×10^{-3}	0.0056 in scientific notation is 5.6×10^{-3}.
7.18	5^2	$(5^4) / (5^2)$ simplifies to $5^{(4-2)}$ or 5^2.
7.19	1/4	2^{-2} is the reciprocal of 2^2, which is 1/4.

7.20	1	7^1 * 7^-1 simplifies to 7^(1-1) or 7^0, which is 1.
7.21	5^5	5^2 * 5^3 simplifies to 5^(2+3) or 5^5.
7.22	7 x 10^2	700 in scientific notation is 7 x 10^2.
7.23	0.0032	3.2 x 10^-3 in standard form is 0.0032.
7.24	1.5 x 10^8	Multiplying 5 x 10^4 by 3 x 10^3 gives 15 x 10^(4+3) or 1.5 x 10^8.
7.25	4^6	(4^3)^2 is simplified to 4^(3*2) or 4^6.
7.26	1/2	2^-1 is the reciprocal of 2^1, which is 1/2.
7.27	8.9 x 10^-5	0.000089 in scientific notation is 8.9 x 10^-5.
7.28	6	(6^3) / (6^2) simplifies to 6^(3-2) or 6^1, which is 6.
7.29	1/27	3^-3 is the reciprocal of 3^3, which is 1/27.
7.30	1	9^1 * 9^-1 simplifies to 9^(1-1) or 9^0, which is 1.
7.31	2^7	(2^3) * (2^4) simplifies to 2^(3+4) or 2^7.
7.32	2.5 x 10^-3	0.0025 in scientific notation is 2.5 x 10^-3.
7.33	750	7.5 x 10^2 in standard form is 750.
7.34	2 x 10^3	Dividing 8 x 10^5 by 4 x 10^2 gives 2 x 10^(5-2) or 2 x 10^3.
7.35	5^6	(5^2)^3 is simplified to 5^(2*3) or 5^6.
.36	1/9	3^-2 is the reciprocal of 3^2, which is 1/9.
.37	7 x 10^-6	0.000007 in scientific notation is 7 x 10^-6.
.38	8^2	(8^4) / (8^2) simplifies to 8^(4-2) or 8^2.
.39	1/256	4^-4 is the reciprocal of 4^4, which is 1/256.
.40	1	6^1 * 6^-1 simplifies to 6^(1-1) or 6^0, which is 1.

Topic 8 – Real Numbers and Pythagoras

8.1) What is a perfect square?

□ A number that has an odd number of factors

□ Any positive number

□ A number that can be expressed as the square of an integer

□ A number that is divisible by 2

8.2) State the Pythagorean Theorem.

□ The area of a right-angled triangle is half the product of the base and height

□ In a right-angled triangle, the square of the hypotenuse is equal to the sum of the squares of the other two sides

□ The sum of the angles in a right-angled triangle is 180 degrees

□ In a right-angled triangle, the square of the longer side is equal to the sum of the squares of the shorter sides

8.3) What is a square root?

□ The number which is squared to give a perfect square

□ A number that can be expressed as the cube of another number

□ The result of dividing a number by 2

□ A number which produces a specific quantity when multiplied by itself

8.4) What is the cube root of 27?

□ 9

□ 3

□ 27

□ 6

8.5) Define a rational number.

□ A number that cannot be expressed as a fraction

□ A number with a finite decimal representation

□ A number that is not divisible by 2

□ A number that can be expressed as the quotient of two integers

8.6) Give an example of an irrational number.

□ 2/3

□ 5

□ 0

□ Pi (п)

8.7) What distinguishes rational numbers from irrational numbers?

□ Rational numbers are only positive, while irrational numbers are only negative

□ Rational numbers cannot be written as decimals, while irrational numbers can

□ Rational numbers are always whole numbers, while irrational numbers are not

□ Rational numbers can be expressed as the quotient of two integers, while irrational numbers cannot

8.8) Which of the following is a real number?

□ 3/4

□ Infinity

□ None of the above

□ The square root of -1

8.9) How does the converse of the Pythagorean theorem differ from the Pythagorean theorem?

□ It only applies to isosceles triangles

□ It is used to calculate the area of a triangle

□ It applies only to equilateral triangles

□ It states that if the square of the longest side of a triangle equals the sum of the squares of the other two sides, the triangle is right-angled

8.10) Which of these is a property of real numbers?

□ They include both rational and irrational numbers

□ They are always integers

□ They cannot be negative

□ They are always fractions

8.11) One leg of a right-angled triangle is 4, and the hypotenuse is 5. What is the length of the other leg?

□ 5

□ 3

□ 2

□ 4

8.12) What is the square root of 144?

□ 14

□ 13

□ 11

□ 12

8.13) If the sides of a triangle are 3, 4, and 5, is it a right-angled triangle?

□ No

□ Sometimes

□ Yes

□ Cannot be determined

8.14) Express the number 1/3 in decimal form.

□ 0.3333

□ 0.3

□ 0.333...

□ 0.33

8.15) What is the cube root of 64?

□ 4

□ 3

□ 8

□ 6

8.16) Is the number √2 rational or irrational?

□ Both

□ Neither

□ Irrational

□ Rational

8.17) Calculate the hypotenuse of a right-angled triangle with legs of lengths 6 and 8.

□ 8

□ 12

□ 10

□ 14

8.18) What type of number is √-1?

□ Real

□ Rational

□ Irrational

□ Imaginary

8.19) If a number is written as 4.5 x 10^-3 in scientific notation, what is its standard form?

□ 0.0045

□ 0.45

□ 0.045

□ 45

8.20) Express the number 0.000123 in scientific notation.

□ 0.123 x 10^-3

□ 1.23 x 10^-4

□ 12.3 x 10^-5

□ 123 x 10^-6

8.21) If one leg of a right-angled triangle is 7 and the other leg is 24, what is the length of the hypotenuse?

□ 26

□ 31

□ 17

□ 25

8.22) What is the square root of 169?

□ 12

□ 13

□ 15

□ 14

8.23) Is the number 0.121212... rational or irrational?

□ Rational

□ Irrational

□ Neither

□ Both

8.24) Express the number 7/8 in decimal form.

□ 0.875

□ 0.88

□ 0.78

□ 0.857

8.25) What is the cube root of 125?

□ 3

□ 4

□ 5

□ 6

8.26) If a right-angled triangle has legs of lengths 9 and 12, what is the length of the hypotenuse?

□ 21

□ 18

□ 15

□ 13

8.27) Express the number 0.000045 in scientific notation.

□ 4.5 x 10^-5

□ 0.45 x 10^-4

□ 45 x 10^-6

□ 4.5 x 10^-6

8.28) What type of number is π (pi)?

□ Rational

□ Irrational

□ Imaginary

□ Real

8.29) What is the result of multiplying 3 x 10^2 by 4 x 10^3?

□ 12 x 10^6

□ 1.2 x 10^6

□ 12 x 10^5

□ 7 x 10^5

8.30) What is the square root of 0.81?

□ 0.9

□ 0.8

□ 0.81

□ 0.091

8.31) Calculate the hypotenuse of a right-angled triangle with legs 10 and 24.

□ 34

□ 20

□ 28

□ 26

8.32) What is the square root of 225?

□ 14

□ 15

□ 13

□ 12

8.33) Is the number 3.14159... (pi) rational or irrational?

□ Both

□ Neither

□ Irrational

□ Rational

8.34) Express the number 4/5 in decimal form.

□ 0.75

□ 0.85

□ 0.9

□ 0.8

8.35) What is the cube root of 216?

□ 8

□ 7

□ 5

□ 6

8.36) If one leg of a right-angled triangle is 8 and the hypotenuse is 17, what is the length of the other leg?

□ 13

□ 9

□ 15

□ 11

8.37) Express the number 0.0000003 in scientific notation.

□ 3 x 10^-8

□ 30 x 10^-8

□ 3 x 10^-7

□ 0.3 x 10^-6

8.38) What type of number is the square root of -4?

□ Irrational

□ Rational

□ Real

□ Imaginary

8.39) What is the result of multiplying 5 x 10^-3 by 2 x 10^-4?

□ 1 x 10^-7

□ 0.1 x 10^-5

□ 10 x 10^-7

□ 1 x 10^-6

8.40) What is the square root of 0.0016?

□ 0.4

□ 0.04

□ 0.16

□ 0.016

Topic 8 - Answers

Question Number	Answer	Explanation
8.1	A number that can be expressed as the square of an integer	A perfect square is a number that can be expressed as the square of an integer.
8.2	In a right-angled triangle, the square of the hypotenuse is equal to the sum of the squares of the other two sides	The Pythagorean Theorem states this relationship for right-angled triangles.
3.3	A number which produces a specific quantity when multiplied by itself	A square root gives a number which, when squared, produces the given quantity.
3.4	3	The cube root of 27 is 3, as 3^3 = 27.
3.5	A number that can be expressed as the quotient of two integers	Rational numbers are those that can be expressed as a fraction (quotient of two integers).
3.6	Pi (π)	Pi (π) is an example of an irrational number as it cannot be expressed as a fraction.
3.7	Rational numbers can be expressed as the quotient of two integers, while irrational numbers cannot	Rational numbers can be expressed as fractions, whereas irrational numbers cannot.
.8	3/4	3/4 is an example of a real number, as it is a rational number.
.9	It states that if the square of the longest side of a triangle equals the sum of the squares of the other two sides, the triangle is right-angled	The converse of the Pythagorean theorem is used to determine if a triangle is right-angled based on side lengths.
.10	They include both rational and irrational numbers	Real numbers consist of both rational and irrational numbers.
.11	3	Using the Pythagorean theorem, the other leg is √(5^2 - 4^2) = 3.
.12	12	The square root of 144 is 12.

8.13	Yes	A triangle with sides 3, 4, and 5 is a right-angled triangle (3^2 + 4^2 = 5^2).
8.14	0.333...	1/3 in decimal form is 0.333...
8.15	4	The cube root of 64 is 4, as 4^3 = 64.
8.16	Irrational	√2 is an irrational number as it cannot be expressed as a fraction.
8.17	10	The hypotenuse of a right-angled triangle with legs 6 and 8 is √(6^2 + 8^2) = 10.
8.18	Imaginary	The square root of -1 is an imaginary number.
8.19	0.0045	4.5 x 10^-3 in standard form is 0.0045.
8.20	1.23 x 10^-4	0.000123 in scientific notation is 1.23 x 10^-4.
8.21	25	The hypotenuse of a right-angled triangle with legs 7 and 24 is √(7^2 + 24^2) = 25.
8.22	13	The square root of 169 is 13.
8.23	Rational	The number 0.121212... is rational as it is a repeating decimal.
8.24	0.875	7/8 in decimal form is 0.875.
8.25	5	The cube root of 125 is 5, as 5^3 = 125.
8.26	15	The hypotenuse of a right-angled triangle with legs 9 and 12 is √(9^2 + 12^2) = 15.
8.27	4.5 x 10^-5	0.000045 in scientific notation is 4.5 x 10^-5.
8.28	Irrational	π (pi) is an irrational number.
8.29	1.2 x 10^6	Multiplying 3 x 10^2 by 4 x 10^3 gives 12 x 10^(2+3) or 1.2 x 10^6.
8.30	0.9	The square root of 0.81 is 0.9.
8.31	26	The hypotenuse of a right-angled triangle with legs 10 and 24 is √(10^2 + 24^2) = 26.
8.32	15	The square root of 225 is 15.
8.33	Irrational	π (3.14159) is an irrational number.
8.34	0.8	4/5 in decimal form is 0.8.

8.35	6	The cube root of 216 is 6, as 6^3 = 216.
8.36	15	Using the Pythagorean theorem, the other leg is √(17^2 - 8^2) = 15.
8.37	3 x 10^-7	0.0000003 in scientific notation is 3 x 10^-7.
8.38	Imaginary	The square root of -4 is an imaginary number.
8.39	1 x 10^-6	Multiplying 5 x 10^-3 by 2 x 10^-4 gives 10 x 10^(-3-4) or 1 x 10^-6.
8.40	0.04	The square root of 0.0016 is 0.04.

Ready for More?

The NWEA MAP testing is adaptive. This means that if your student found these questions too tricky or too easy, they may find it useful to practice grades below or above they grade they are in. This will expose students to new concepts and ideas, giving them a better chance at scoring higher in tests.

Alexander-Grace Education produces books covering Mathematics, Sciences, and English, to help your student maximize their potential in these areas.

For errata, please email
alexandergraceeducation@gmail.com

Made in the USA
Las Vegas, NV
27 December 2024